Colby House - Headquarters,
Ordnance Survey of Northern Ireland

Mountjoy - Headquarters,
Ordnance Survey of Ireland

The front cover shows Colby - the father of Irish
Ordnance Survey mapping - framed by reflections of
the evolution of map-making in Ireland: from
Plantation mapping in 1622 to the satellite technology
of today.

*...every Prince should have...a Draught of his Country and Dominions,
to see how the ground lies in the several parts of them,
which highest, which lowest; what respect they have to one another,
and to the sea; how the Rivers flow, and why; how the Mountains lie.*

Thomas Burnet, The Theory of the Earth (1684)

An illustrated record

of

Ordnance Survey

in

Ireland

This book has been researched and compiled by
the staff of both Ordnance Surveys in Ireland

© The Ordnance Survey of Ireland 1991

© The Ordnance Survey of Northern Ireland 1991

Published jointly by:
Ordnance Survey of Ireland
Ordnance Survey of Northern Ireland

Printed by the Ordnance Survey of Ireland, Phoenix Park, Dublin.
Collating and binding by Criterion Press Ltd, 74 Dublin Industrial Estate, Dublin 11.
ISBN 0-904996-02-6

CONTENTS

OFFICERS IN CHARGE AT MOUNTJOY

1824-28	Major W Reid
1828-46	Captain T A Larcom
1846-52	Captain J Cameron
1852-53	Captain W Yolland
1853-54	Lieutenant-Colonel H Tucker
1854-61	Lieutenant-Colonel G A Leach
1861-76	Lieutenant-Colonel B A Wilkinson
1876-79	Major C W Wilson
1879-81	Lieutenant-Colonel C N Martin
1881-83	Colonel R H Stotherd
1883-84	Colonel Sir C W Wilson
1884-85	Major J C MacPherson
1885-86	Colonel Sir C W Wilson
1886-88	Lieutenant-Colonel A B Coddington
1888-89	Captain Shaw
1889-96	Lieutenant-Colonel Kirkwood
1896-98	Major R C Hellard
1898-99	Major G H Sim
1899-1903	Major Haynes
1903-05	Colonel G H Sim C.B.
1905-06	Lieutenant-Colonel A D Meeres
1906-09	Major R U H Buckland
1909-13	Lieutenant-Colonel C C J Pery
1913-18	Lieutenant-Colonel G F A Whitlock
1918-22	Lieutenant-Colonel J E E Craster

ASSISTANT DIRECTORS
ORDNANCE SURVEY OF IRELAND

1922-35   Captain C H Mew
1935-64   Colonel N MacNeill
1964-73   Commandant G Madden

Mr M C Walsh
Director of Operations
1973-

CHIEF SURVEY OFFICERS
ORDNANCE SURVEY OF NORTHERN IRELAND

1922-33   Captain W Carlielle
1933-49   Mr W M Gilmore
1949-57   Brigadier K M Papworth O.B.E.
1957-70   Lieutenant-Colonel W R Taylor O.B.E.
1971-77   Mr C G T Bere

Mr M J D Brand
Director 1977-

ACKNOWLEDGEMENTS

FOREWORD

'Whereas you have represented unto Us that it will be advantageous to Our Service to raise an additional Company of Royal Sappers and Miners to be employed in the operations of the Survey in Ireland...' An extract from George IV's Royal Warrant which marked the beginnings of the Irish Ordnance Survey.

Born of the need for accurate land measurement for valuation purposes, the Irish Ordnance Survey under Lt.-Col. Colby completed the world's first large-scale mapping of an entire country by 1846. However, the survey had been primarily a townland survey and the maps were not detailed enough for a proper valuation, so a more informative series was completed by 1867. From Fair Head to Mizen Head, and from Howth Head to Slyne Head every road and track, every stone wall and hedge, every river and stream, every house and barn had been surveyed and mapped. Sir Richard Griffith and his team could plot their valuations.

Limelights and 200-pound weight theodolites, measuring chains and water levels - these were the tools of the early surveyors' trade. Throughout the length and breadth of Ireland, mountain tops were illuminated by limelights used as markers for angular observations establishing a framework for the survey. The field surveyors' plots became printed maps by the careful eye and delicate touch of draughtsmen, engravers and printers, using quill pens and Chinese inks and copper plates.

That first 6-inch survey was followed in time by further editions and by larger- and smaller-scale maps, accepted by all as authoritative representations of the topography of Ireland. But the old production methods have long since gone. Technical developments in the twentieth century have transformed the Survey's work, and limelights and chains have given way to electronic distance measuring equipment, satellite positioning systems, aerial photography and computers.

This book marks the 200th Anniversary of Ordnance Survey. It is not a detailed history of Ireland's map-makers; rather it is a pictorial record of the evolution of surveying and mapping in Ireland, and in particular the role of the Ordnance Survey in Ireland since 1824. It is a remarkable story.

It is dedicated not just to Colby, Drummond, Larcom and O'Donovan who began it all, but to all Ordnance Survey staff in Ireland, past and present: the field surveyors and draughtsmen; engravers and printers; and today's map-makers with their computers and databases and remote sensed data; craftsmen all - those who were and are Ordnance Survey.

MICHAEL J D BRAND - Director OSNI, Belfast
MUIRIS C WALSH - Director of Operations OSI, Dublin

IRLANDIAE by Baptista Boazio c 1599

This book proposes to give a flavour of the activities, successes and trials of the Ordnance Survey since it was established in Ireland in 1824. There is a wealth of Irish mapping prior to the formation of the Survey which stretches back to Claudius Ptolemaeus c 150 A.D. and a few colourful examples are included here to set the scene.

Boazio's map of Ireland was chosen for the opening page since it predates the establishment of the Ordnance Survey in 1791 by nearly the same time that this book celebrates - 200 years. Only three original copies are recorded: one in private hands printed on silk, one in the British Museum and one in the Library of Trinity College in Dublin. Very little is known of Boazio or his reasons for compiling this map, but it is interesting to note the lack of detail outside the "pale" towards the north and west of the island.

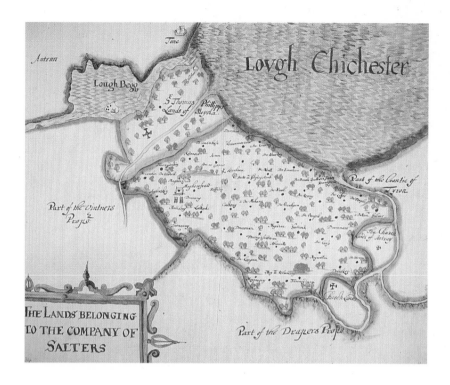

Plantation map by Sir Thomas Phillips 1622

During the early 17th century large tracts of land in Co Londonderry were awarded to the London trades companies. The example shows Magherafelt and Lough Chichester - now Lough Neagh.

After the Cromwellian wars, Cromwell's soldiers were to be paid in lands forfeited by his enemies. A survey was undertaken to define the confiscated lands and William Petty was given charge of the project in 1654. Essentially the survey contains the name, acreage and boundary of each forfeited townland, and it owes its title to the fact that data was plotted "down" in map form. Many of the original maps were destroyed, but copies of most are held, including those that perished, by the National Library of Ireland and the Public Record Offices in Belfast and Dublin.

Portion of William Petty's Down Survey 1654-1658

8

Petty's general map of Ireland 1685

Petty planned to extend the Down Survey and include the unforfeited lands to the west and north to allow him to publish an atlas. This project proved too ambitious and the atlas eventually included only the counties, provinces and a general map shown here. It was engraved in Amsterdam and printed in London, and finally published in 1685 under the title "Hiberniae delineatio". The general map was at a scale of 12 Irish miles to an inch and the atlas provided the basis for several small scale maps of Ireland over the next 150 years.

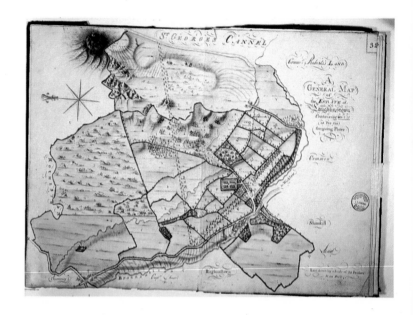

Estate Map of Loughlinstown Co Dublin by Michael Kenny 1770

Large scale maps as we know them were not available at this time so landlords of large estates commissioned surveys of their properties for many reasons: to portray their importance to their peers, or as an aid to managing their property, or for the sale of the property. Many examples have survived and they are both colourful and varied in design.

The British rule of law in Ireland was always under threat so a good map was required by the military authorities to plan their operations. General Sir Charles Vallancey in his capacity of Director of Military Engineeers in Ireland met the need by completing a number of maps between 1776 and 1796. An original copy of one of these is now held by the Ordnance Survey of Ireland in Dublin.

Portion of Vallancey's 1785 map of Ireland

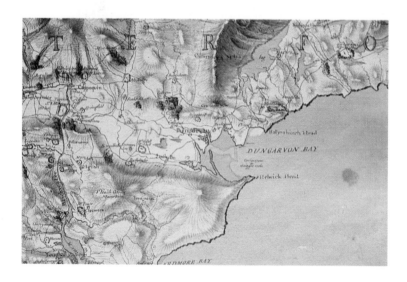

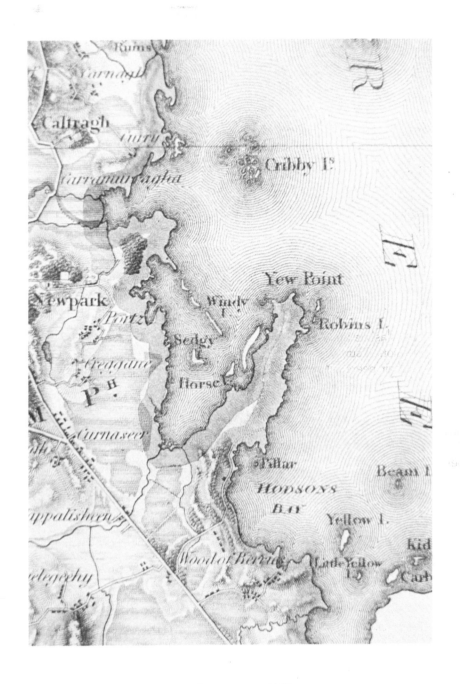

Portion of Griffith's Grand Jury map of Roscommon 1817

The forerunners of County Councils were Grand Juries and they commissioned surveys of their areas of responsibility mainly for the building and maintenance of roads. Two Grand Jury maps were prepared for County Roscommon: William Edgeworth completed the northern part of the County and Richard Griffith the southern part, a portion of which is shown here. The mapping of this era was much varied in design until later when the Ordnance Survey applied a standard specification for the original six inch survey.

The Tower of London by Thomas Malton, 1792

The Ordnance Survey was established in 1791 with its headquarters in the Tower of London under the Master General of the Board of Ordnance. Its function was to produce maps for military use initially of the coastal areas along the south of England in preparation for an expected invasion after the Napoleonic wars. The first of these maps was completed in 1801 at a scale of one inch to one mile. The associaton with the Board of Ordnance eventually led to the acceptance of the name Ordnance Survey, which is unique to the three mapping organisations in these islands.

THE EARLY DECADES OF ORDNANCE SURVEY IN IRELAND

Early in the nineteenth century it became obvious that the local taxes in Ireland, which were called the County cess and based on townland units, were inequitable. Successive committees of the House of Commons debated the problem and found that although the names and outlines of these divisions were assumed to be well known, the acreages and rateable valuations were doubtful. Finally on the recommendations of the Spring Rice Committee a survey of all Ireland at a scale of 6 inches to one mile was authorised by the British Parliament in 1824.

On the 22 June 1824, the day after the report was signed, Lt Col Thomas Colby was chosen to undertake this task. Prior to this the Ordnance Survey's brief had been topographic mapping at smaller scales and this departure marked the introduction of the large scale mapping that was to become the major task. Colby immediately began the trigonometrical survey and on one of his early visits to Ireland he selected Mountjoy House in the Phoenix Park as his headquarters.

Lt. Col. Thomas Colby

Mountjoy House, Phoenix Park, Dublin by Sheelagh Duff

Mountjoy House was originally built by Luke Gardiner as a private residence in 1728, and later used as a cavalry barracks to provide a mounted escort to the Lord Lieutenant resident nearby in the Viceregal Lodge (now Áras an Uachtaráin).

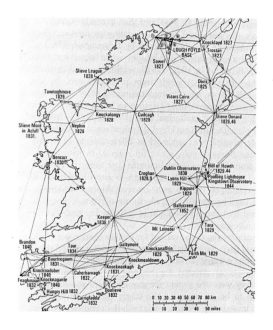

The first task to be completed was to precisely calculate the positions of a framework of points upon which the mapping could be based. This was done by a process of triangulation whereby sightings were taken to distant mountain tops using theodolites.

Some of the primary triangles in Ireland have sides greater than 150 kilometres in length and the argand lamps previously used by the survey were found to be not bright enough over these distances.

The Principal Triangulation of Ireland

Lieutenant Thomas Drummond invented the limelight in 1825 which not only allowed these great distances to be eventually observed but was also used widely in the entertainment business for stage lighting, etc. Drummond was also instrumental in greatly improving the heliostat reflector which was used for observations by day. Portlock's trigonometrical party finally completed the triangulation in August 1832.

Diagram of Drummond's Limelight

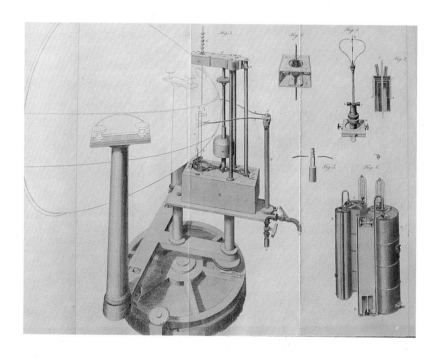

Drummond had unique talents as an inventor and mathematician which the survey harnessed during these formative years; and he was recognised outside surveying circles when described in Wordworth's correspondence as 'Drummond of calculating celebrity'.

Thomas Drummond
by Henry Pickersgill

The principal triangulation of Ireland was executed mainly using two large theodolites, one three feet and one two feet in diameter. The three foot instrument was constructed by the celebrated Ramsden at the close of the eighteenth century, and the two foot instrument was constructed and supplied to the Survey by the Troughton and Simms firm in 1828.

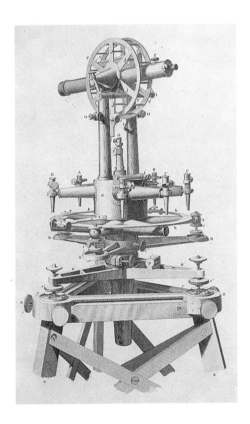

The 2 foot theodolite

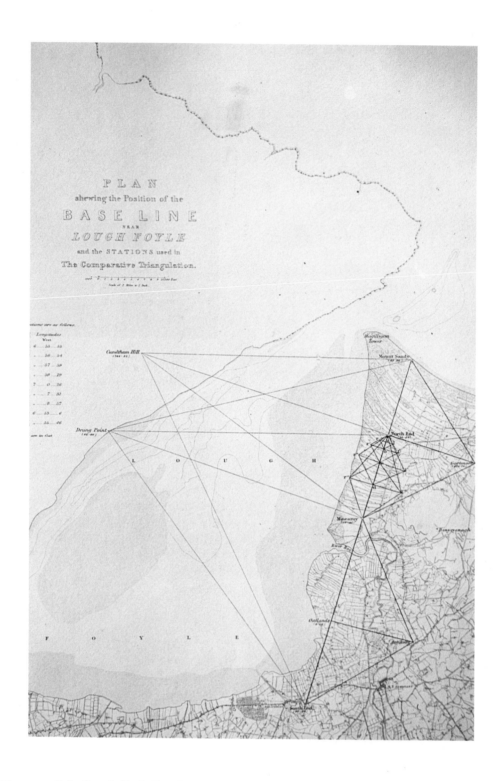

Diagram of the Lough Foyle Baseline

In order to compute this network of triangles, the length of one leg of one triangle needed to be measured. The leg chosen was along the shores of Lough Foyle and this measured distance is known as the baseline.

Colby's Bars

The accuracy of this measurement was paramount since it set the scale for the whole survey. Previous methods used for baseline measurement were not acceptable by Colby, so Drummond was tasked in the spring of 1826 to initiate experiments. Finally Colby himself suggested using the compensation principle with parallel bars of two metals (ie iron and brass), and Drummond developed the idea and came up with a design towards the end of 1826. The bars were connected in the middle with steel tongues fixed across the ends which were free to shift according to the expansion or contraction of each bar. This allowed the coefficient of expansion of the metals to be used in the calculation of distance. Some of the bars used in Ireland were subsequently used to measure bases in the Cape of Good Hope and on Salisbury Plain in England, and one bar remains in the Ordnance Survey in Dublin.

Observing the baseline under tenting

The measurement of the baseline began in 1827 and was observed under tenting to minimise fluctuations in temperature. The bars were mounted on tripods and the total distance of 7·89 miles which included the crossing of the River Roe was completed in November 1828 after 60 days of measurement by 70 men. The accuracy achieved is still marvelled at today.

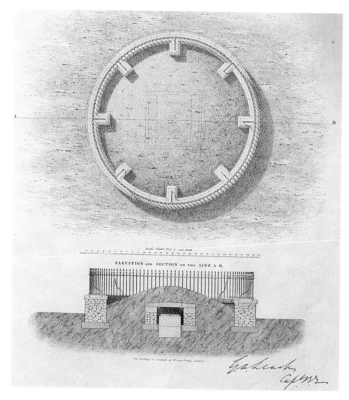

*Diagram of
Base Towers*

ELEVATION and SECTION on the LINE A-B.

Towers which contain the exact end-points of the line measured were built at each end of the baseline. The northern end was extended to Mount Sandy near Magilligan Point by trigonometrical means, and a fourth tower was also built at Minearny, north of the River Roe. Sadly only three of these towers have survived to the present day, as coastal erosion resulted in the tower at Mount Sandy being lost to the sea. The southern-most tower was recently engulfed by urban expansion of Ballykelly and is now a focal point in a public recreation area.

Base Tower at south end as it is today

Royal sappers and miners surveying in 1837

A major debate raged in the early 1820's as to whether civilian or military surveyors would be employed on the impending survey of Ireland. The Spring Rice Committee decided the issue by recommending that the task be given to the Ordnance Survey under Colby's direction. Colby began preparations, immediately sending sappers and miners of the Royal engineeers on a course of instruction in surveying and mathematics to Chatham, and the first survey parties took to the field in the northern counties early in 1825.

Each district commander observed a secondary trigonometric network using 12″ theodolites so that two or three points lay within each parish. 7″ or 8″ theodolites were used to densify the network of triangles to make one or two points accessible to each townland. Chain lines were run between the trigonometrical stations thus giving a check between the chained distances and the trigonometrically computed distances.

Chain line plot

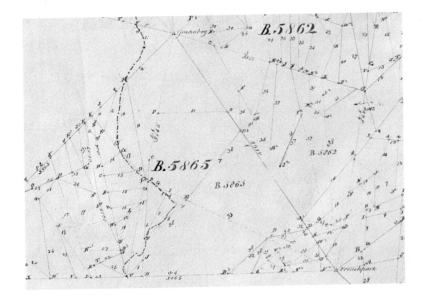

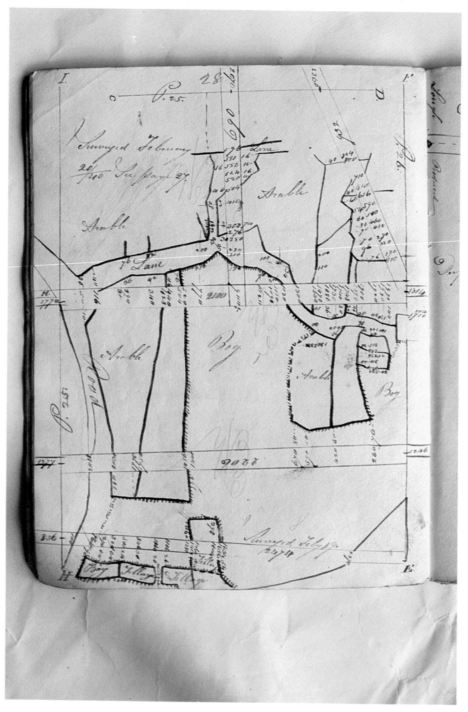

Content field book

The theodolite triangles were then further subdivided into chain triangles which were laid out to fit as snugly as possible into each townland. The books used by the field survey parties to note their observations were called content field books which contained two main elements. Firstly, the content register listed the areas of the triangles used to calculate the areas of the townland.

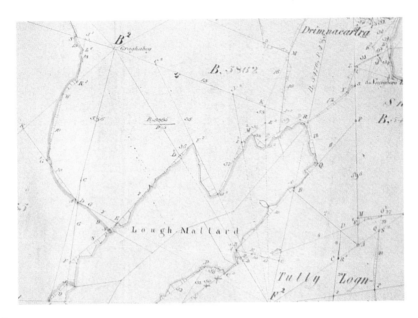

Content Plot

Secondly, the content plot contained the townland boundaries plotted by offset measurements. Other major topographical features were also included at this stage.

The final manuscript drawing called the fair plan was then completed. This included all the other topographic features except field boundaries which were specifically excluded from the specification by the Spring Rice Committee. These fair plans were compiled on a parish basis, with north at the top, at a scale of 6 inches to one mile, and engraving began in 1827. Initially there did not seem to be any provision for combining the parishes into a regular rectangular map series. This decision was taken in 1828, and records from this period do not provide the reasons for the decision.

Fair
Plan

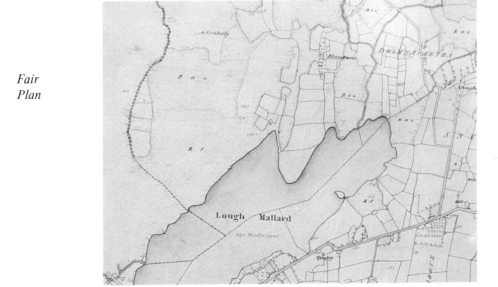

A new boundary department was established by Act of Parliament in July 1825. The Irish civil engineer, Richard Griffith (who previously surveyed the grand jury map of south Roscommon mentioned earlier) was appointed head of the new department and he was directly responsible to the Lord Lieutenant in Dublin Castle. This department was tasked with ascertaining the boundaries of parishes and townlands in Ireland. His staff liaised with Colby's surveyors in the field to indicate the positions of the boundaries to enable Ordnance Survey staff to survey and plot the boundaries.

Richard Griffith

Griffith's produced boundary descriptions and sketch maps of all the townlands and parishes in the country and in 1830 his department was given the task of valuing the townlands as well as delimiting them. Finally Colby's and Griffith's departments would provide the acreages and the valuations required for an equitable tax system.

Boundary description

Boundary sketch

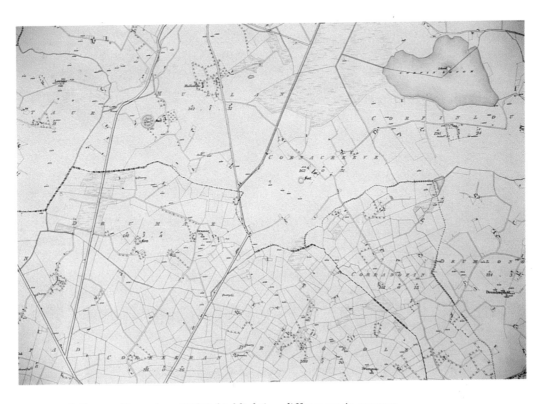

6" map of County Monaghan (1835) highlighting differences in content

As stated earlier field boundaries were specifically excluded by the recommendations of the Spring Rice Committee. Manuscript plans and some engravings of the early and mid 1830s were dotted with minute strokes where fences crossed or joined townland boundaries and other features. Finally in October 1835 as a result of a request which highlighted the different standards, Colby ordered that leading fences should appear on the plans in future to assist Griffith's staff when plotting their valuations. The appearance of all hedges and fences marked an important stage in the progress of the 6 inch survey. However, nearly all of Ulster and parts of the surrounding counties required a revision to include the missing detail.

Lieutenant Thomas Aiskew Larcom R.E., took over as administrator in Mountjoy in 1828 having spent a short period on field duties. Larcom had an interest in broadening the scope of the survey to record details on history, commerce, geology, natural history, etc., and to publish the results on a parish and finally a county basis. The first parish of Templemore, Co Londonderry, was finally published in November 1837 but got a hostile reception due to its size (350 pages for one parish), its disjointed compilation, and the fact that it cost £1,700 which was more than three times the original budget for one county.

T.A. Larcom R.E.

Funding for the project was cancelled as a result, although data collection continued for many of the northern counties due to Larcom's personal interest. Today this memoir material is an invaluable historical record, and further memoirs of some parishes have been published in the recent past by local historical societies and community groups.

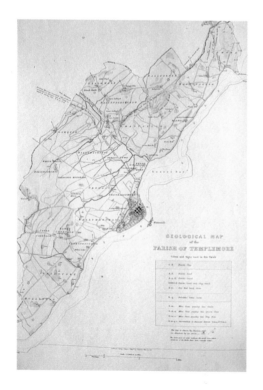

Geological map of the parish of Templemore, Co Londonderry

By 1830 the Survey began to recruit staff to research geographical names and authorise the standardised forms of the names which were to appear on the maps. The most famous of these researchers was John O'Donovan who was a bright, humorous workaholic and was arguably one of the greatest Irish scholars of all time. Lacking the class consciousness that inhibited some of Colby's officers, O'Donovan had no difficulty in drawing information from all levels of society. He was subsequently appointed as Professor of the Department of Celtic at Queen's University of Belfast.

John O'Donovan
by Charles Grey

Namebooks for the Parish of Aglish, Co Mayo.

The vast majority of the names originated in the Irish language and the standardised forms were to be anglicisations. Placenames are among the best documented features of the original six inch survey and they are compiled on a parish basis. The forms thus provided by the Ordnance Survey have served as official government orthography in the English language.

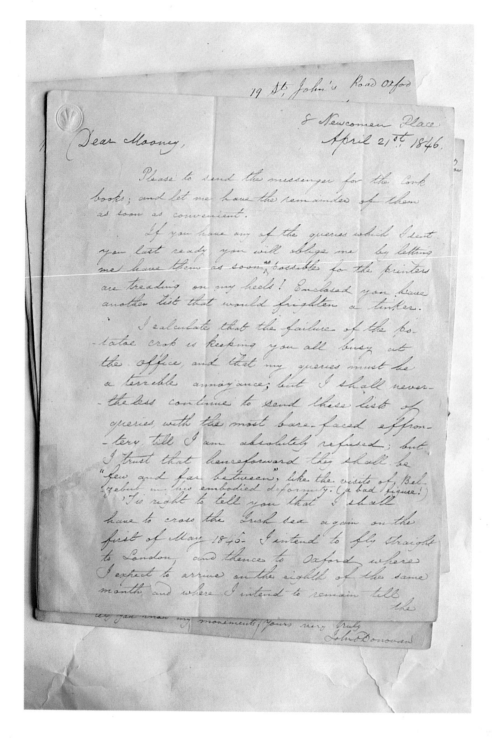

One of O'Donovan's Letters

O'Donovan was a prolific writer and his letters, both private and official, are famous for their witicisms and flowing descriptions of particular facets of life at the time. The sample shown, written in 1846, makes reference to the potatoe famine and, as well as being entertaining, displays the stresses of his heavy workload.

To facilitate drainage and other engineering operations it was decided to put height points on the finished maps. Local datums where the heights were fixed at zero were chosen at different locations around the country. The datum for County Dublin was fixed at the low water mark of the spring tide on the 8 April 1837 at Poolbeg lighthouse. Discrepancies were later found between adjoining local systems, and the Dublin datum was adopted nationally nearly five years later.

Prior to this, heights were computed from vertical angles observed between trigonometrical stations in selected east-west lines and related to sea level at each end of the lines. This method was superseded in 1839 by using spirit levels along major roads and taking observations to three decimal places of a foot.

An early level displayed by Mr M O'Gorman, OSI

The primary network of spirit levelling related to the datum at Poolbeg lighthouse in Dublin was completed in 1843 and was used extensively until the datum was changed to mean sea level at Malin Head, Co Donegal in 1958.

The principal lines of spirit levelling completed in 1843

Types of bench marks used by the Ordnance Survey in Ireland

Bench marks (widely known as "crows feet") related to the datum are sited on walls, public buildings, bridges, etc. along the road network. Stone masons carved "crows feet" and these marks became part of folklore throughout Ireland. These "crows feet" are still being cut in Northern Ireland and have only recently been replaced by a range of metal bolts in the Republic of Ireland. Many of these old marks are still in existence and where found by the modern day levelling parties are included in the new network.

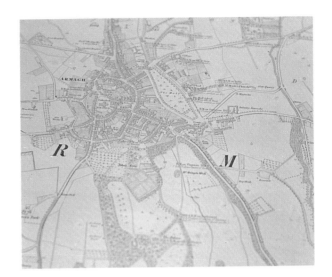

Copper plate of 6" map of Armagh

The fair plans of separate parishes were eventually combined and engraved. Copper was used rather than steel to allow corrections to be made and the map image was engraved in reverse for the impression-printing presses of the time. An average of sixty engravers was employed in three groups to produce the outline, the writing, and the ornament. Many mechanical engraving tools were invented by this group during the 1830s such as hand punches, spring punches, etc., which were later used in England and America.

The copper plates were first heated, then inked, and the surplus ink cleaned from the plate. The inked plate was then laid face up on the press, moistened paper laid on top, and a fine blanket on top of that again. This was then passed through the rollers of the press transferring the image to paper. The printed sheets were then placed in milled glazed boards under pressure to smooth and dry.

The copper plate press in use in Dublin in 1991

First proof

The first print from a copper plate was known as the first proof which was then thoroughly examined. A list of alterations was drawn up and the plate was passed back to the engravers to effect the changes. Remark number 89 in the illustration requests that the name "DEER PARK" be deleted and this name did not appear on the published copy.

Ireland was the first country in the world to complete national coverage of a map series at this unprecedented large scale. As publication progressed southwards during the 1830s the quality of the engraving and the correct proportioning of the relative strengths and sizes of the outline, the writing, and the ornament, produced a work of great artistic beauty and merit.

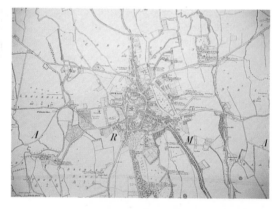

The final published map at 6″ scale

The fireproof store as it is today

A fire proof store was built in 1827 to house the fair plans and the documents relating to the survey. Recently much of this documentation was handed over to the National Archives for posterity.

TOWN PLANS AND DERIVED MAPPING

Unpublished 5-foot town plan of Newtown-Stewart 1833

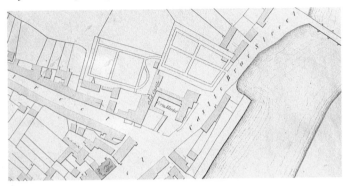

Separate town plans at 12 inches to one mile were advocated by the Spring Rice Committee, but Colby gave no guidance to his Officers which resulted initially in a plethora of different scales: Londonderry at 24 inches to one mile, Belfast at one inch to 3 chains, and Newry at 12 inches to one mile. None of these was large enough for Griffith who requested a scale of 4 foot to one mile. Colby finally suggested 5-foot which being ten times the 6-inch scale was easier to adapt to his draughtsmens' instruments. Serious inaccuracies became evident when plotting at 1:1056 from the 6-inch fieldbooks, so a resurvey of the towns became necessary.

The town plans were produced for Griffiths valuers and were not intended to be published. There were 33 sheets of the 5-foot plan of Dublin, and Larcom had the Castle sheet engraved and published in 1840 - the first town plan published by the Ordnance Survey. This sheet won praise from many quarters and helped to stimulate public opinion in favour of publishing 5-foot plans of other urban centres.

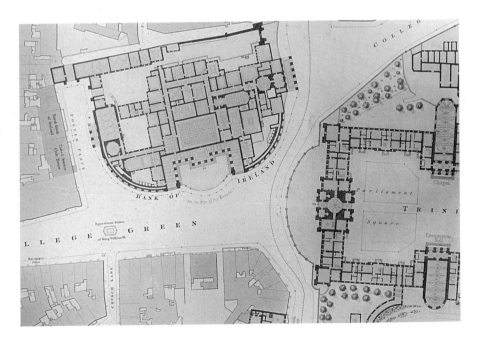

The 5-foot Castle sheet published 1840

Revised 5-foot of Kilkenny first published in 1871

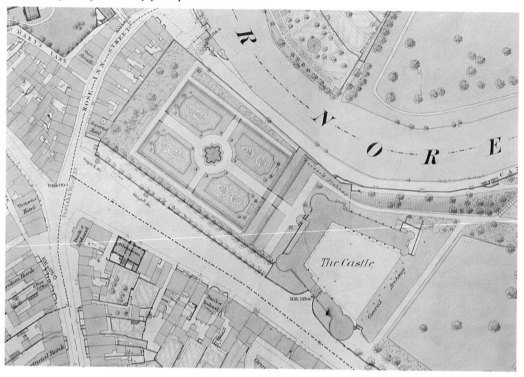

Colours were added by hand by thirteen and fourteen year old boys some of whom were paid as little as sixpence a day. The coloured sheets were sold for five shillings and the plain for two shillings.

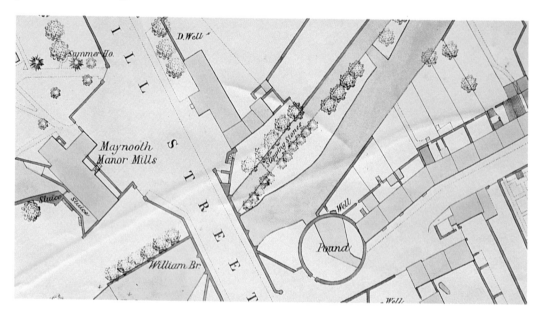

10 foot of Maynooth, surveyed in 1872 and zincographed in 1874

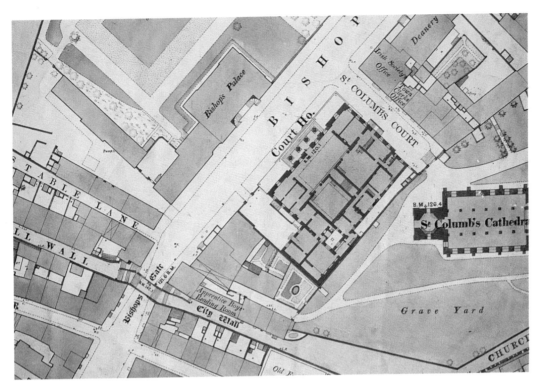

10-foot of Londonderry 1873

Between the years 1857 and 1879 a scale of 1:500 or 10 foot to one mile was introduced for urban plans although not totally, and the 5 foot scale was restored after 1879. Copper engraving of the urban plans was replaced when zincography began in Dublin in 1861. The decline of town plans began in the 1870s when interior walls (except in buildings of special public importance) were dropped, and other minor features such as flower beds and isolated trees also disappeared.

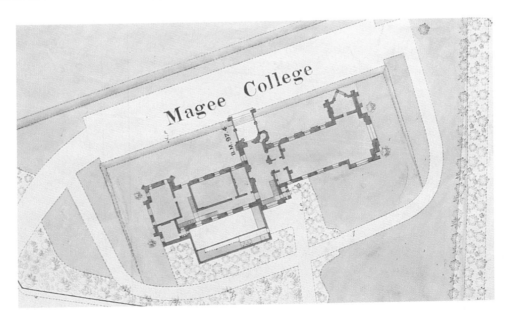

*Card Revision
of the 6-inch*

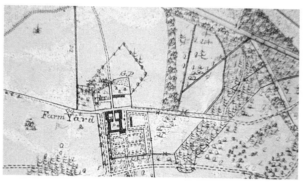

Revision of the 6-inch series began in 1845 and for some of the northern counties this amounted to a resurvey based on the original trigonometrical skeleton. These updates' (including the results of the town surveys of the 1850s and 1860s) were then engraved on copies of the original copper plates which were created by electrotyping.

First edition Irish 1" series published from 1855 to 1895

The Irish one inch series was authorised in 1851 as a base map for geologists and the first map appeared four years later. It was produced as a black outline edition, or with hachures in brown as shown on the illustration, and it was derived from the original 6-inch maps or their revised editions.

Larcom had a general map of Ireland published in 1839 at ¼-inch to one mile for the railway commission. The southern counties were compiled from pre-Ordnance Survey mapping since their field surveyors had not progressed this far south at that stage. As a result of this the Ordnance Survey refused to put its name to the map which later became known as the railway map. These first-edition ¼-inch maps, produced from 1887 to 1899, were derived from Ordnance Survey's own 1-inch series.

First edition, Irish ¼-inch series published from 1887 to 1899

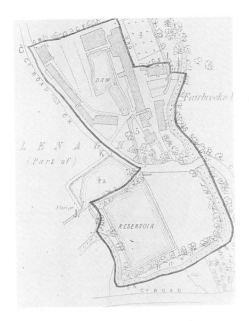

Landed-estate map 1869

After the potato famine many Irish Landlords were forced by economic pressure to sell their properties and an Encumbered-estates Court was established in 1849 to deal with the flood of land transactions. The judges found the 6-inch too small for the precise area calculations required and eventually the Survey was asked to supply estate maps which were paid for by the proceeds of the land sales. These estate maps were replotted at 1:2500 from the 6-inch fieldbooks and then field-revised.

1858 Test Production at 1:2500 in Co Wexford

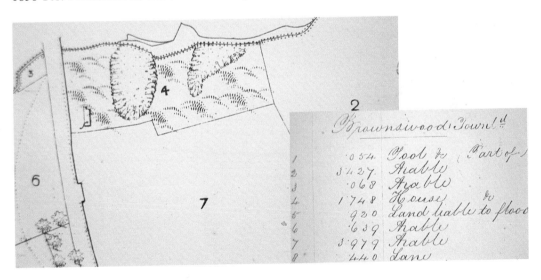

In 1858, the Director of Ordnance Survey Sir Henry James, had maps, an area book and title page printed for an estate in Co. Wexford. However he had second thoughts and left them unpublished. In 1863, Griffith requested the town plan of Dublin be extended into the suburbs, and the Survey complied by resurveying the whole county and publishing by parish at 1:2500 scale.

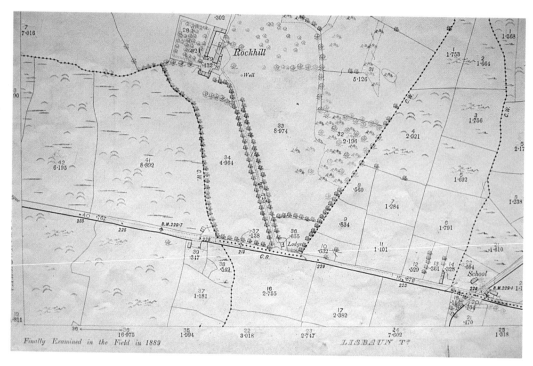

Early map at 1:2500 of Co Roscommon 1889

The resurvey of Ireland at 1:2500 was finally authorised in 1887 after much debate over the previous thirty years. It was based on the same primary triangulation as the earlier 6-inch survey and uses the same projection with county origins. Sparsely occupied regions such as mountains and moorlands were omitted and the survey was completed in 1913.

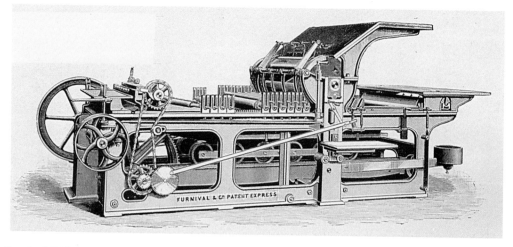

Furnival Lithographic Printing Machine

The new series at 1:2500 consisted of over 19,000 maps and a lithographic printing machine was purchased for printing this increased volume. This allowed the maps to be prepared "forward-reading", rather than the previous reverse-engraving method.

Lithographic Stone

Around the turn of the century there was an attempt to popularise some of the smaller scales by printing in colour. Both zincography and lithographic stones were used to maintain registration while printing, and almost all coloured Irish maps of this era were printed in Southampton.

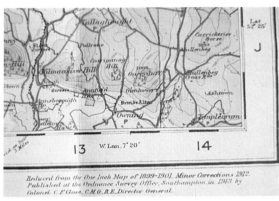

First edition ½-inch Series, 1917

A 16-sheet second edition of the ¼-inch series was published in colour in the 1900s; a new ½-inch series was published between 1912-18 with layer colouring; and a multi-colour 1-inch Tourist map of Killarney was published in 1913 and received wide acclaim.

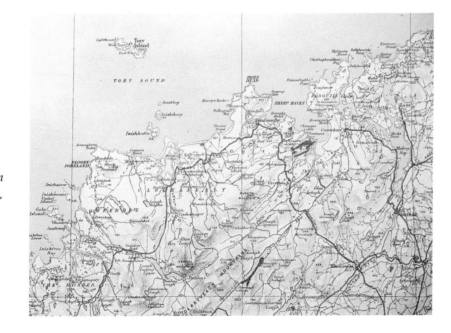

Second edition ¼-inch Series, 1904

A map of Ireland at a scale of ten miles to one inch (1:633 600) showing the river catchment basins was first published in 1868. This scale has been much used since as a base for thematic maps showing mineralogical deposits, electricity stations, rural and urban districts, baronies, and an index to the 6-inch County series. In 1920 this scale was also used for a coloured map showing peatbogs and coalfields from information supplied by the Geological Survey of Ireland.

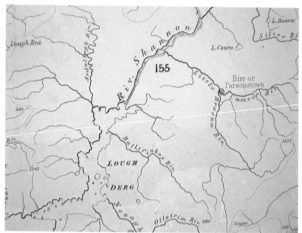

Map of Ireland showing river catchment basins 1868

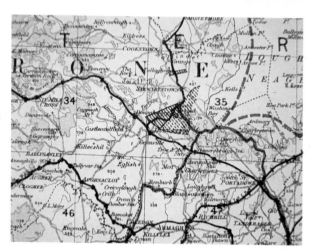

Map of Ireland showing peatbogs and coalfields 1920

Map of Ireland showing Railways 1944

38

The division of Ireland in 1922 resulted in the emergence of separate Ordnance Surveys: the original body, which had been responsible for mapping Great Britain and Ireland, now confined to Great Britain; the Ordnance Survey of Northern Ireland, established on 1st January 1922, with headquarters at "Laurine", 342-4 Antrim Road, Belfast; and a third, Ordnance Survey based at "Mountjoy" in Phoenix Park in Dublin which, by 1st April, had taken responsibility for the survey of the rest of Ireland. The three bodies shared a common goal: to provide and maintain a network of mapping of the highest possible quality on a national basis.

*Ordnance Survey
Dublin*

Both Irish organisations, now civilianised and attached to their respective Ministries of Agriculture in Belfast and Dublin, continued with the work of revising the 1:2500 surveys - Ordnance Survey cf Northern Ireland in County Londonderry, and Ordnance Survey of Ireland in County Cork.

In the early years OSNI staff numbered about 45 under Capt. Carlielle, while in Dublin Capt. C H Mew commanded a complement of 214.

*Extract from contemporary
1:2500 Map of Belfast*

*"Laurine" as it is today
OSNI HQ 1922-1933*

The first change of note for Ordnance Survey Dublin, was the transfer, in 1924, for administrative purposes, from the Department of Agriculture to the Department of Finance under the directorship of the Commissioner of Valuation.

Valuation Office
Ely Place, Dublin

Later in Northern Ireland, during a period of relative inactivity, mainly due to limited resources, OSNI's position in the Ministry of Agriculture also came under scrutiny; but it was not until 1933 that the decision was taken to transfer the organisation to the Ministry of Finance where it came under the control of the Commissioner of Valuation who was also designated Boundary Surveyor.

Armagh House, Belfast
OSNI Headquarters 1933-1967

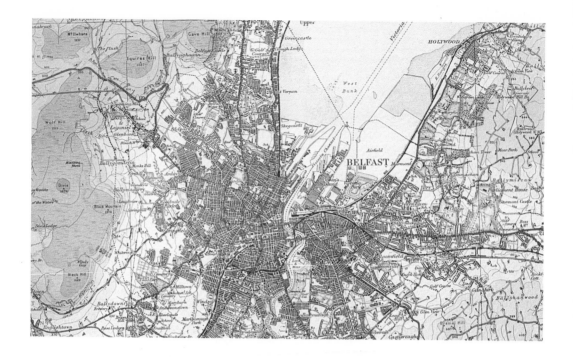

Extract from first edition of the
1" Series

Belfast initiated a major break with tradition in
1938 when the new One Inch edition was
introduced. On completion it was to cover
Northern Ireland and adjoining parts of the
Republic of Ireland in 11 sheets, rather than the
43 sheets of the original series, the larger sheet
size perhaps reflecting the growth of motor
transport and the widening horizons of the
public in general.

City Hall, Belfast

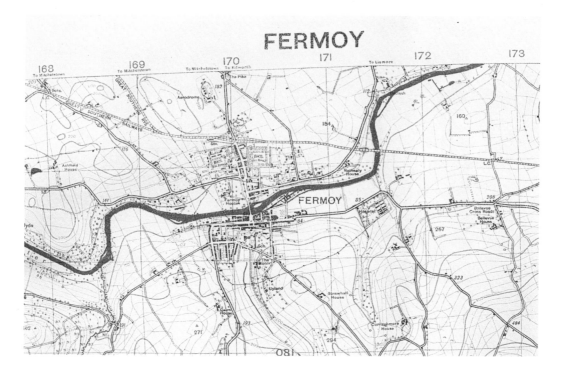

FERMOY

New publications were also introduced by Dublin. A series of maps at 1:20 000 scale was derived from a revision at 1:2500. Sadly, only eight maps were published before the project was abandoned. The example shows a coloured map of Fermoy, originally published in 1934 and reprinted in 1939.

The weir at Fermoy

Belfast Bomb Damage Scene

The outbreak of war in 1939 brought considerable change to OSNI. Normal duties were largely held in abeyance and were to some degree replaced by surveys more directly related to the war effort.

Of the 80 staff in post just before the war, 40 men volunteered for service in the forces and 7 were seconded to the drawing office of Harland and Wolff's shipyard. The remainder were employed on surveys in connection with Tillage, Valuation and Bomb damage in Belfast. The provision and conservation of turf (peat) as a fuel source assumed a new importance in the light of the war effort and to this end the Turbary section was augmented, in 1943 and again in 1944, by more staff. The surveyors' job was to ensure equitable allocation of turf to successful applicants by surveying and marking on the ground the limits of each plot, and to record this information on 1:2500 maps for official records.

Ploughing for Victory.

Turf Cutting

GB 53 75 c

Nur für den Dienstgebrauch

n. Bild Nr. F 228/40/II/111 (I II. 5)

Belfast

Wasserwerk Belfast

Länge (wesll. Greenw.): 5° 56' 55"   Breite: 54° 37' 20"

Mißweisung: 14° 19 (Mitte 1940)   Zielhöhe über NN 50 m

Genst. 5. Abt.   Dezember 1940

Karte 1 : 100 000

Irl. 5

Maßstab 1:10 000

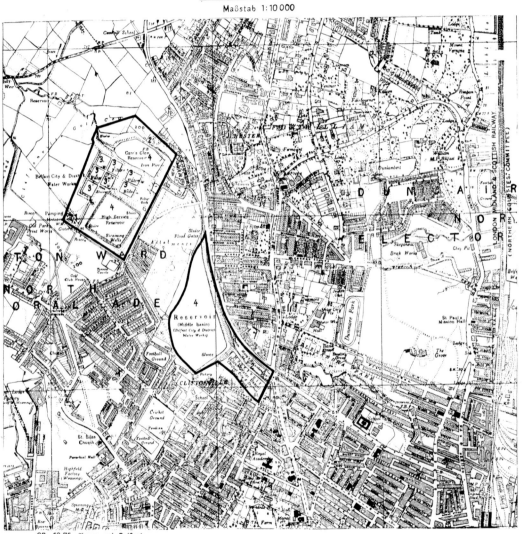

GB 53 75 Wasserwerk Belfast
1) Pumpanlage   etwa   550 qm
2) ansch. Pumpanlagen etwa   400 qm
3) 7 Filterbecken
4) 4 Rohwasserbecken   _____
            bebaute Fläche   etwa   950 qm

Gesamtausdehnung etwa 350 000 qm

Luftwaffe Target File

The Luftwaffe made use of Ordnance Survey maps in planning their target areas for bombing Belfast as evidenced by this German overprint on a six-inch map which they had brought to 1:10 000 scale.

45

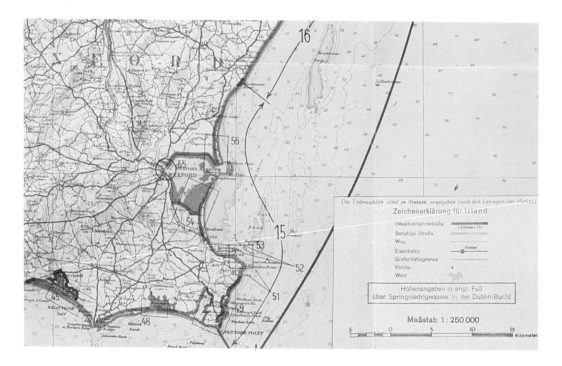

Invasion Map of Ireland

The strategic importance of Ireland did not escape either Germany or Britain. The Germans considered the invasion of Ireland as a stepping stone to Britain, drawing up plans including maps, photographs and booklets of detailed information. On this extract from a 1:250 000 which was derived from Ordnance Survey mapping, the coast has been colour coded to indicate its suitability for landing troops.

Profiles of the coastline were also drawn in preparation for a possible sea-landing operation.

Coastal Profile

The British Forces compiled a third edition of the 1 inch series by combining groups of four of the Ordnance Survey's 1 inch maps, adding a grid and overprinting in four colours. A black and white series at 1:25 000 scale was also compiled from the 6 inch series in preparation to counter the invasion threat.

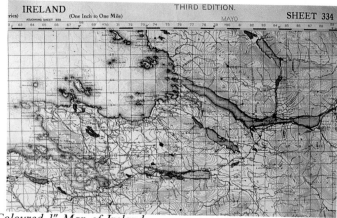

Coloured 1" Map of Ireland

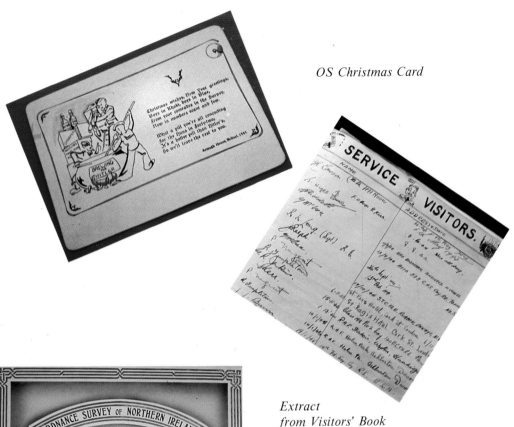

OS Christmas Card

*Extract
from Visitors' Book*

As the war progressed those who served overseas kept in touch with their former colleagues, and Ordnance Survey bulletins were sent to inform friends abroad of developments at home. The sense of camaraderie and "belonging" shown at this time has always been in evidence among the staff of Ordnance Survey

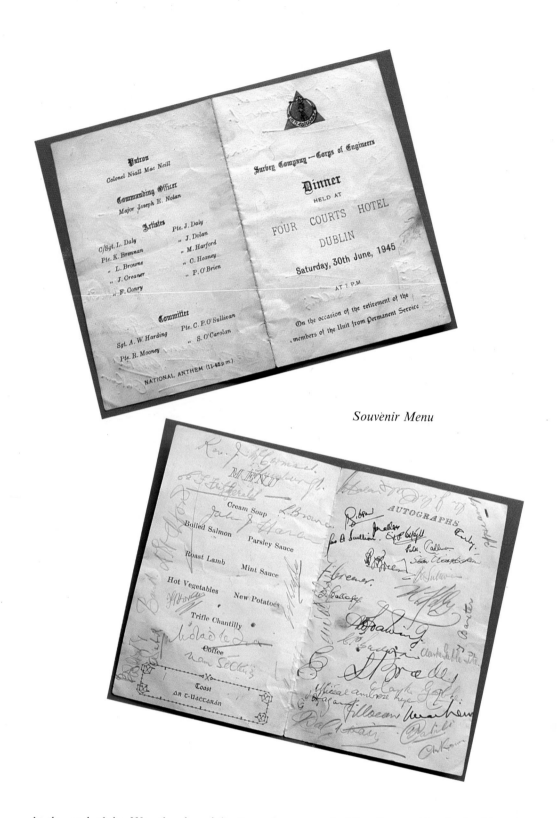

Souvènir Menu

At the end of the War the demobilisation of personnel of the Survey Coy in the Phoenix Park was celebrated with a dinner in the Four Courts Hotel, Dublin. The menu for the occasion speaks for itself.

Northern Ireland was an important staging post on the fringes of Europe for allied troops.

This extract from the 1945 revision of Co Antrim shows how accommodation for the troops changed the Northern Ireland landscape........

B-17 Bomber - The famous "Flying Fortress"

.....and the significance of the war effort at home was also reflected in the construction of service airfields such as Langford Lodge, which was a major armament depot for the US airforce.

Here is the site as it appears on a post-war Irish Grid 1:10 000 sheet.

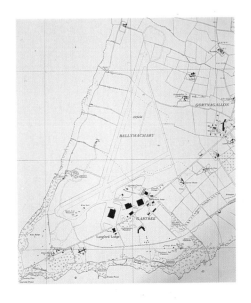

49

THE NATIONAL MAPPING NETWORK

Brigadier K M Papworth, the Chief Survey Officer for Northern Ireland, produced a major report on the state of the Ordnance Survey of Northern Ireland mapping programme and made recommendations for its improvement, in which he suggested some radical changes which still have an effect today. This was followed by a report by the Advisory Committee on Mapping Requirements in the Republic of Ireland. These reports included among their recommendations the recasting of all mapping in Ireland on to the Transverse Mercator projection and the introduction of a common reference system.

The original 19th Century large-scale mapping used a projection with a separate origin for each county and this had resulted in distortion at county boundaries making it impossible to accurately join the maps of adjacent counties. This problem was to be overcome by casting all future mapping on the Transverse Mercator projection with a central meridian for the whole Island.

All Irish mapping produced since these recommendations were adopted is related to the Irish Grid.

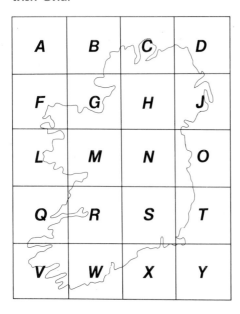

The Irish Grid

50

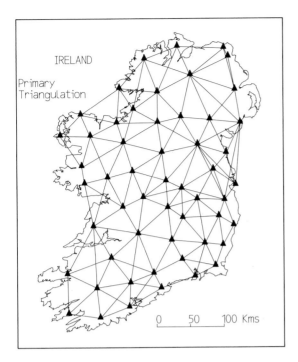

Primary Retriangulation Network

In 1950 work commenced in Northern Ireland on a retriangulation to form a framework for the new series of Irish Grid large scale maps. Ordnance Survey of Ireland began their retriangulation in 1959. Many of the points observed in the principal triangulation of the nineteenth century were incorporated in the new scheme. Triangulation stations, in the form of the familiar concrete pillars seen on many hill-tops, were erected. The Irish Grid co-ordinated values of triangulation points are available to the public and are used in many engineering and other special surveys.

Triangulation Equipment

One of the problems was transporting heavy equipment up to some of the highest mountain tops in Ireland and here donkey-power is being used for the job.

Triangulation Pillar

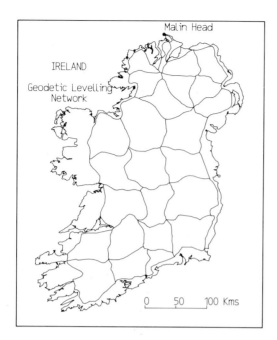

The original levelling of the 1840s' and the subsequent work circa 1890 contained some discrepancies between various lines of levels. To overcome the problems thus created, new geodetic levelling was completed, followed by the observing of secondary and tertiary lines to provide a homogeneous level network.

All large-scale mapping in Northern Ireland now carries levelling information related to the Mean Sea Level datum at Belfast. All other levelling in the island including that of small scale maps of Northern Ireland is related to MSL at Malin Head in Donegal. The difference between Malin Head datum and Belfast datum is less than 2 centimetres.

Geodetic Network

Tide Gauge Belfast

S 500 Level

Technological advances in spirit levelling have not been as dramatic as in other areas of surveying. Automatic levels have been in use for some time now and continue to give good service. The leveller, who previously had to book his readings, today enters them into a data logger.

Leveller at work

Many thousands of Bench Marks (the familiar "crow's feet") throughout Ireland, hand-cut on stone bridges and dwellings, form a dense framework of very accurately heighted points for planners and engineers.

Crow's Foot in use

To ensure a homogeneous plan and height control network for the whole country the instrument observations are computed using a rigorous adjustment. This work was originally carried out laboriously using hand cranked calculators and books of mathematical tables.

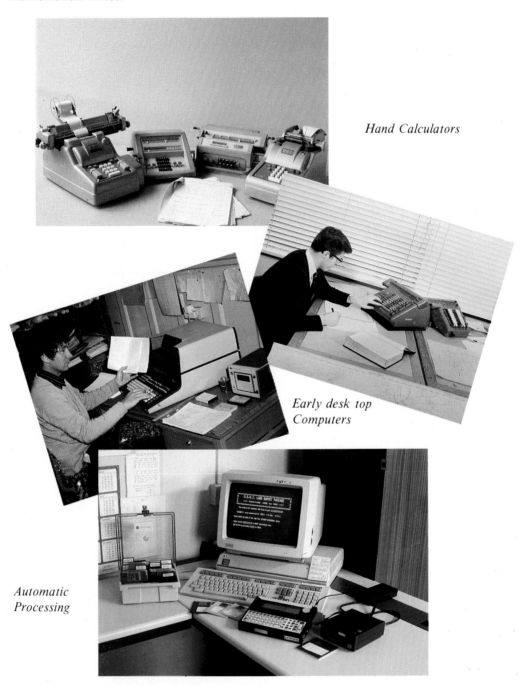

Hand Calculators

Early desk top Computers

Automatic Processing

The arrival of the desk top computer in the 1970s revolutionised the system and enabled much faster processing of information resulting in a significant reduction in staff required for the job. Today field data is collected in a logger, downloaded to disc and sent to Headquarters for automatic processing and plotting.

The excellence of OS products is the result of long tradition and the expertise of staff. Skills and techniques are handed down through intensive training in all aspects of the work, from cartography to field survey.

This school of the 1950s is learning the techniques of 1:1250 survey and the discomfort of plotting on site.

The surveyor also has to learn to ignore (if possible) distractions such as this audience of schoolboys.

THE NEW LARGE-SCALE SURVEYS

The large-scale survey began in the early 1950s and this is the first Irish Grid plan which was completed by OSNI in 1954. The plan was drawn on Whatman's paper which was soon to be replaced by plastic. In Dublin the programme for producing large-scale plans on the Irish Grid began in the mid 1960s.

PLAN 130-15 SW

Manual Cartography

On this extract, the blue key made direct from the field surveyor's plate can be seen. This was the guide for the draughtsman whose job it was to "fair draw" the manuscript. The names, annotations, etc, were hand-typed and the ornamentation hand-drawn. When photographed for printing, the blue on the manuscript disappeared, leaving only the black as drawn for publication.

Hand ornamentation

Surveyor measuring a shop front, with his sketching case carried on his shoulder.

For generations the surveyor worked in the field on a special tracing paper but documents were subject to distortion and the accurate transfer of detail to a manuscript copy in the drawing office was difficult. A more stable base was required and from the start of the urban Irish Grid survey the medium on which the graphic surveyor worked was a metal plate, coated on the drawing surface with white matt enamel. In the early years the primary control for 1:1250 survey was co-ordinated revision points (RPs) fixed by traverse methods. These points were plotted on the plate followed by detail, picked up by a subsequent chain survey. The rest of the topographic detail was then supplied by the surveyor who carried the large one-piece 16-hectare plate in a sketching case. By graphic methods, using tape and optical square, brass drawing point, scale and set square he added the houses, fences, streams, vegetation and all the other features to be shown. In addition he collected all the street names, house names and place names and annotated the wide variety of other features mapped.

By the late 1950s the Butt-joint plate was in use. This was a more rigid metal plate, still enamel coated, but having the advantage of allowing the topographic detail to be drawn continuously across the edges by locking the plates, four at a time, in a specially constructed sketching case. As surveying progressed, the plates were removed and replaced in the case so that one continuous and borderless plan was the result.

In the early 1960s the enamel plate gave way to plastic as the material for the field working document and the top illustration shows a surveyor from this period. Note the new plastic document is oblong in shape compared to the square Butt-joint plate.

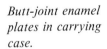

Butt-joint enamel plates in carrying case.

Section of 1:2500 Map

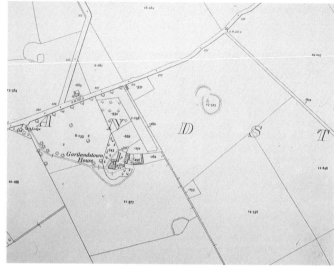

Here a surveyor is seen plotting in the field on a plastic document which has the advantages of being stable, suitable for working on with a fine pencil and not easily damaged by rain, one of the surveyor's occupational hazards.

The surveyor plotting on site

The new plastic material was used for field documents from the early stages of the 1:2500 scale revision programme begun in the 1960s. Most of the country had not been updated for many years and in addition much change had taken place in the post-war period, so the rural mapping was badly out of date. At this time the old County Series maps were recast on the Irish Grid and any discrepancies resulting from the operation were dealt with by the Field Surveyor. In Belfast, as the 1:2500 maps were revised they were photographically reduced to 1:10 000 scale for the Irish Grid series which was to replace the 6-inch map.

As the country was resurveyed or revised for the new Irish Grid maps the growing public demand for up-to-date map information was recognised and the old system of cyclic revision was replaced by Continuous Revision. The new system allowed areas of change to be revised promptly after development occurred with priority given to areas required by customers.

Surveyor revising new housing development.

The up-to-date information is made available to those who require it through a copy of the surveyor's Master Survey Document.

Today's map today

NEW MAP PRODUCTION TECHNIQUES

Map production also changed in the 1960s and the traditional method of drawing with pen and ink as a means of producing the finished manuscript was superseded by scribing. In this new technique an impression of the surveyor's field work was printed on a sheet of plastic which carried a coating of emulsion. The implement used had a steel or sapphire cutting point which was directed manually along the lines of detail, slicing into the emulsion and resulting in the creation of a map in negative form – the linework translucent and the background opaque.

Scribing

This method had the advantage of producing a line with absolutely consistent gauge and the consequent benefits of greater speed and economy.

Scribing tool

The negative was then photographically converted to positive form on film, and names, boundaries, building infill, and vegetation were added.

Accurate measurement of land areas has been practised by Ordnance Survey from its earliest days. Using the large-scale surveys, the various "parcels" of land as defined by their topographical boundaries such as hedges, walls, etc, are measured individually and the resultant values are published on the map.

The original method, accurate but costly, required the use of a gridded transparent overlay and a sliding scale operated by hand. Each parcel was measured twice to minimise the risk of error.

Early "scale-and-trace" measurement

This method gave way to others in which a succession of machines was employed, the equipment becoming more compact and more sophisticated over the years.

Automatic planimeters

In today's digital mapping system the calculation of area values is entirely automatic. The operator has only to identify the parcel and the computer supplies the value. An unique identifier enables each area value to be accessed by the user.

Efficient map production requires the support of an up-to-date Reprographics Group and both organisations installed modern equipment and developed new skills to meet the needs of the time.

The increased scope provided by the new equipment also led to a greater ability to respond to customer needs, particularly planners, engineers, etc, for Advance Revision Information, enlargements, reductions, transparencies and prints of various drawings, whether map-based or otherwise. In Dublin paper manuscript copies of large-scale mapping were rectified to their original dimensions using the cartographic camera for recasting on the Irish Grid before field revision.

Cartographic Camera

In 1967 Ordnance Survey of Northern Ireland moved to a new headquarters built to their requirements at a cost of £131,000. Situated in Ladas Drive, about 2 miles from Belfast City Centre, the building was to house all the Ordnance Survey office staff as well as the field surveyors responsible for the Belfast region.

At this time overall responsibility for Ordnance Survey Northern Ireland was transferred from the Commissioner of Valuation to the Chief Survey Officer.

OSNI Headquarters,
Ladas Drive 1967-85

During the early 1970s printing in Dublin was scattered throughout three buildings using four printing presses and two proofing presses, some of which dated from the 1890s. A new building was specially commissioned to house small scales, print process, a photo studio and a modern print shop. At the same time three new two-colour printing presses and a guillotine were installed and this considerably extended the Survey's ability to meet customer demand.

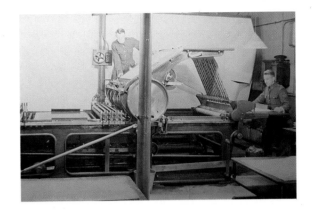

Old Furnival Press

*New Print Building
Officially opened 1977*

*Two-colour print
machine*

SURVEY METHODS ADVANCE

Aerial photography had long been used as a source for small scale mapping information when OSNI first took delivery in 1958 of a block of large-scale survey plotted under contract by a commercial company using stereo plotters. A short time later stereo plotters were installed at Dublin and Belfast but with photography supplied by a commercial company. In the early 1970s both Surveys acquired aerial cameras and now capture photography for Ordnance Survey use and under contract to other organisations. Flight navigation and camera operation is carried out by Ordnance Survey staff.

Below is an extract from a report of the first sortie flown by OSNI from Aldergrove. The conditions were not suitable for photography, but as a trial run it proved worthwhile. Since then the "side sighting" has been replaced by a new forward-view navigation sight.

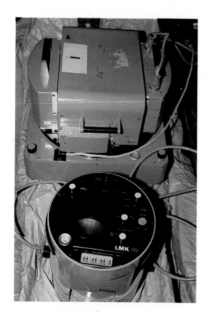

Camera

used in OSI

Most of the ground features are plotted from the aerial photographs and this greatly reduces field survey work compared with previous methods.

A series of overlapping photographs

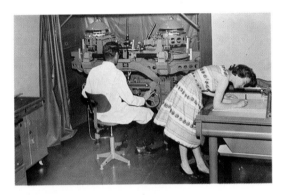

Stereo-plotting - early 1960s

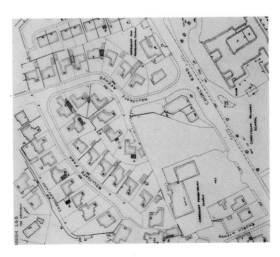

Section from aerial photograph

Photogrammetric plot ready for graphic survey completion

Master Survey Document completed in the field

What is not clear from the illustrations is that, when overlapping photographs are viewed stereoscopically, height differences can also be seen. It is therefore possible to plot contours from aerial photography. Over the years both Surveys have built up extensive archives of vertical aerial photography, and contact prints and enlargements are on sale to the public.

Changes were also taking place in ground survey techniques and the late 1950s and early 60s saw the introduction, by both organisations, of Tacheometric equipment. These instruments enabled the optical measurement of both bearing and distance thereby considerably speeding up the process of traversing. They also had the benefit of broadening the scope of the operation to allow the observation of a dense network of points for use as a framework of control for subsequent completion by the detail surveyor. Supplying a control network for the detail surveyor by this method greatly reduced the time and cost of field completion compared with the previous method of taped traverses with chain line and off-sets.

Tacheometric Observation form

The instrument

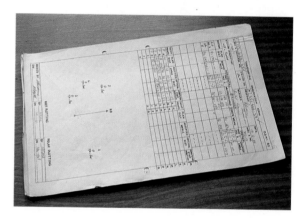

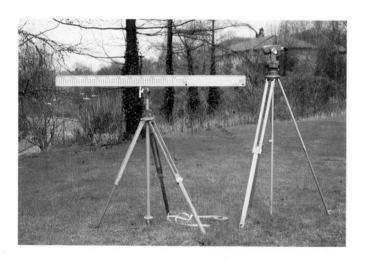

Tacheometric equipment

66

The arrival of tellurometers, the first electronic distance-measuring instruments used by the Surveys in Ireland, made a significant impact on the fixation of survey control points. Much of the secondary and tertiary triangulation in Ireland was completed using Tellurometers.

Remeasuring Colby's base

Tellurometers were extensively used by both Ordnance Surveys until the mid-1970s.
In 1960 OSNI surveyors remeasured Colby's base at Lough Foyle by Tellurometer. They achieved in less than an hour's actual measuring time what took Colby's engineers two summers to complete. When compared, the results differed by 1″ in a distance of nearly 8 miles!

Air-lifting equipment for pillar building

A whole new generation of Electronic Distance Measurers (EDM), which used infra-red rather than radio waves, became available in the late 1960s. Ordnance Survey continued its long tradition of adopting new technology which was "right" for the job. These new instruments, attached to a conventional optical theodolite, were ideal for laying down a dense network of detail control for the graphic surveyor.

With a distance reading cycle of just a few seconds the urban surveyors problems caused by traffic crossing sight lines were minimised.

Plotting board and equipment

Further improved instruments produced a readout of horizontal distance, and a system was developed for plotting, on site, much of the information acquired. A tripod-mounted plotting table with a 24″ diameter 360° protractor was devised. A scale, secured by a pin to the centre of the protractor, enabled observed bearings and distances to be plotted on a document. To safeguard accuracy the points were selected in such a manner as to ensure that the plotting was self checking.

The illustration shows the equipment at a very early stage of development which was quickly replaced by a more sophisticated table and scale.

Direct Plotting had a relatively short life span, being phased out as data loggers and automatic plotters became available to produce more cost-effective surveys. Instruments continued to develop and today's surveyors use the Total Station which records and displays all station data and observations giving the option of on-board data storage or connection to a data logger.

The illustration shows a Total Station and a target prism. The prism, which can also be hand held, reflects the instrument signal for measurements of distance and height.

Instrument and target prism

Total Station

The system employed in Ireland is geared to the use of a separate data logger which stores the digital data for subsequent down-loading to disk, for automatic processing and plotting.

Today the latest space-age technology, the Global Positioning System (GPS), is being used for surveying. GPS uses satellites to calculate three-dimensional co-ordinates for locations on the ground. Receivers collect and decode information broadcast from a series of satellites which allows a ground position to be calculated. When data is collected from two or more positions simultaneously with one receiver sited on a point with known co-ordinates the position of the other point can be calculated very accurately to satisfy survey control requirements. The use of the equipment is not affected by weather conditions and siting is not restricted as in the conventional way by the need for clear sight-lines between points. A clear view of the sky is all that is required, and this gives the surveyor much more scope in the selection of points reducing time and cost for the work.

Global Positioning system

Field observing

Downloading data to computer

SPECIAL SERVICES

In the early 1960s, both organisations with resources and expertise available could broaden the scope of their activities. The creation of the new town of Craigavon in Northern Ireland established a need for 1:500-scale engineering surveys showing ground features in much more detail than was possible at smaller scales.

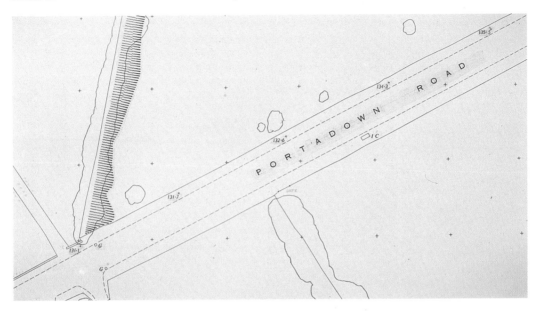

The resultant maps showed the position of manholes, inspection covers, water valves and hedge and tree overhangs. Other areas of potential development were also surveyed and mapped at 1:500 scale.

By the late 1970s the Surveys in Belfast and Dublin were undertaking a wide variety of special tasks, largely for government departments. Factory sites, road schemes and stretches of river under investigation, all required individual treatments. Scales of survey up to 1:200 were used to show street furniture, cross and longitudinal sections of roads and water courses and inverse levels in drains in factory sites. Coal stock volumes are regularly calculated by both Ordnance Surveys using digital photogrammetry techniques. All such surveys are carried out to the precise specification of the commissioning bodies.

The illustration shows surveyors taking levels along the bed of a river and a longitudinal section plot.

Moneypoint,
Co. Clare

Northern Ireland has a large number of Government sponsored Factory Estates at different stages of development, and in the early 1970s the Department's Engineers became alarmed that the records of underground plant were not as complete or accurate as required. Ordnance Survey undertook a programme, which was to last a number of years, to provide a series of reliable drawings. The basic large-scale Ordnance Survey map was used as the base (Master Plan) with derived drawings produced at 1:1000 scale (As Built) and at 1:500 scale (Services Plan). Ordnance Survey staff surveyed the additional features required and worked in co-operation with the Civil Engineeers to collect information relating to the various services before compiling the finished drawings. The value of this mapping will be realized over many years with planners, engineers and the contractor on site benefiting from reliable information.

1:1000 As Built

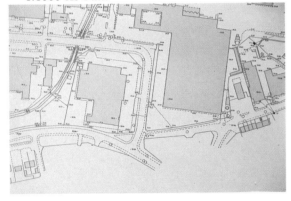

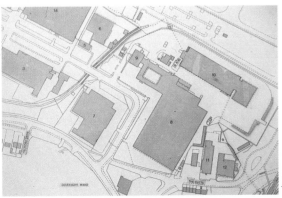

1:500 Service Plan

1:1250 Urban Plan

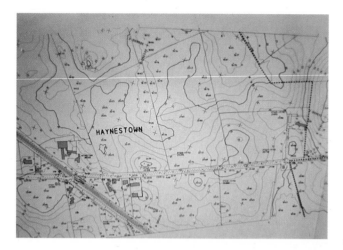

1:1000 survey with 0·5m contours.

Digital Terrain Model

Engineering surveys for road planning and construction are carried out to the usual high standard set by Ordnance Survey to comply with the customers' detailed specifications. Drawings are supplied on stable plastic and where required digital terrain models are provided to accommodate the flexible use of the survey data in site selection and design. The illustrations show work carried out by Ordnance Survey Dublin in connection with a major road scheme.

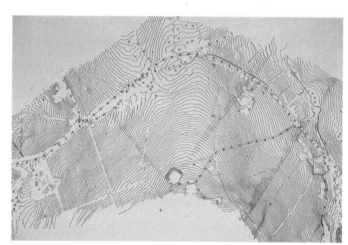

Western Parkway Motorway

Colour Vertical Tralee, Co Kerry

In addition to in-house requirements, aerial photography is supplied as a special service to customer specification. Both organisations are equipped with precision aerial cameras, primarily for in-house use, and photograhy is flown under contract for clients as time and resources allow. A photographic archive is maintained at both Survey Headquarters and prints or diapositives are on sale to the public.

False Colour - Infra Red

Ordnance Survey Northern Ireland broke new ground in the 1970s when they were awarded a contract by Ordnance Survey Great Britain for the scribing and letter-pressing of 1:2500 scale maps, thus creating a considerable number of new jobs. This expansion, unforeseen at the time of the move from Armagh House, forced the acquisition of additional accommodation which was once again in the centre of Belfast. The contract was subsequently extended to include 1:10 000 work and lasted for nine years.

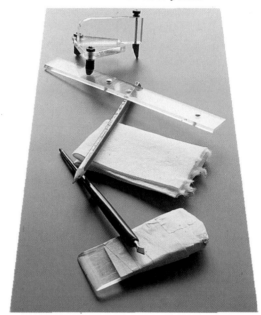

Accommodation for Agency at Clarendon House

MAP RELATED ACTIVITIES

*Aerial Photograph of
Dromore Mound*

All features likely to be of archaeological
significance were surveyed and shown on the
early 6-inch maps of the country. Extensive use is
made of these maps and subsequent editions for
the identification of sites in archaeological
research.

In Northern Ireland the field surveyors record
the current state of sites at revision, and the
Historical Monuments Branch of the
Department of the Environment co-operate with
Ordnance Survey in selecting and naming the
archaeological features shown on new
publications.

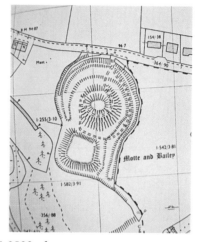

Feature as shown on 1:2500 plan

In Dublin an Ordnance Survey Archaeological Branch was established in 1947 to
undertake a national survey of megalithic tombs. Five volumes have already been
published and three more are in production. A further three volumes are planned - two
dealing with the tombs in Northern Ireland and a national one devoted to passage tombs.
Close liaison is maintained with the Department of the Environment in Northern Ireland
and the archaeological section of the Office of Public Works in Dublin.

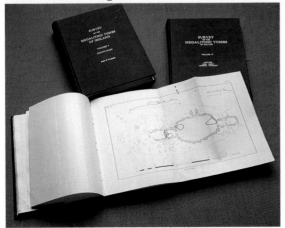

Published Volumes

Shanid Castle, Co Limerick

Colour oblique aerial photography of selected archaeological sites has been flown on a commercial basis by OS Dublin over the last few years.

The original 6-inch survey of Ireland was primarily to map all townland boundaries and record their names. These townlands, the units on which today's larger administrative areas are often based, are shown on all modern large-scale maps. The boundaries are delineated in great detail with the names spelt exactly as for the first 6-inch map.

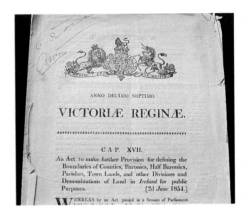

Local Government District Map 1984

Ordnance Survey produce special administrative maps to show Local Government Districts and Parliamentary Constituency areas.

Boundaries shown on maps

At the original survey of Ireland great care was taken with the collection and recording of place names such as townlands, districts, hamlets and hill features and this tradition has been carried on through the years. Today the Ordnance Surveys in Ireland are regarded as the custodians of these names and they are published on successive editions of maps in their original form.

New name   -   Gilnahirk Park

All other names on Ordnance maps are revised for each new edition. Changed, obsolete and new names are carefully recorded with the authority for form and extent documented. The illustrations show the documentations relating to a typical name change.

Name change -
Wellington College

In Northern Ireland most rural roads are named. They are published on OS maps as authorised by the local authority.

A Placenames Branch
was established in Dublin
in 1955 to research and
establish the correct Irish
forms of geographical
names. Maps of all
periods are of immense
value as research sources
and historical
documentary evidence is
assembled by the branch
for each name. Most of
the names researched
are townlands and the
new 1:2500 National Grid
series is bilingual. A

series of books on the original forms of townland
names in Northern Ireland is currently being compiled
by the Department of Celtic at the Queen's
University, Belfast. Both Ordnance Surveys are co-
operating in the project.

Recent publications specific to placenames include a bilingual edition of the 1:250 000
Ireland North map, a gazetteer of Ireland, and a book listing the historical evidence for
the townlands in County Limerick. It is hoped that the Placenames Branch will take
delivery of a computer system later in the year to facilitate the recording and retrieval of
their research data.

Published Volumes

SMALL SCALES

The one-inch standard series in its various coloured and black and white formats was a popular and much used map in Ireland for generations from its introduction in the mid-nineteenth century. By the mid-1930s some of the editions were badly out of date so in Northern Ireland a new larger-size series was commenced and by 1938 the first two sheets of this Popular edition had been published. Dublin also published four new one-inch district maps covering major tourist areas. In 1958 the third-edition one-inch series replaced the Popular edition and gave sterling service until being phased out in 1978 when the first 1:50 000 map was published.

One-inch map

One-inch District map

Half-inch map

The half-inch map has been maintained through the years in its various formats and continues to be a firm favourite.

By the mid 1970s the old one-inch maps required extensive revision and replacement of printing plates so a decision was taken to produce a metric series for all of Ireland at the universally-recognised scale of 1:50 000. The first of these was published in 1978 using conventional cartographic methods, and the Northern part of the country was completed by 1985.

*Extract from OSNI 1:50 000
Sh 29 "The Mournes"*

*Extract from OSI 1:50 000
Sh 78 "The Reeks"*

OSI used digital methods when they produced their first 1:50 000 sheet in 1988, and work on the remainder of the series is progressing.

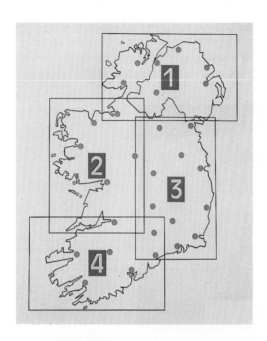

Tourism is a major industry in Ireland, North and South,and a 1:250 000 Holiday Map series covering the whole island in four sheets was produced with the first sheet, Ireland North, published in 1980.

The co-operation that has always necessarily existed in the production of small-scale maps was taken a step further by agreeing a common specification for the series.

FOUR HOLIDAY GUIDE MAPS OF IRELAND

This is more than a map. It's a holiday guide, designed to add interest to your travels around Ireland.

Whether you're on a motoring tour or exploring cross-country, this map shows you how to get there because nearly every motorable road is shown — including motorways, trunk, main and secondary roads. And they're all clearly marked and easy to follow.

Planning your itinerary is therefore made as simple as possible.

All the places marked come to life on the back of the map. There you'll find details of museums, stately homes, cathedrals, antiquities, forest parks, National Trust properties, country parks and nature reserves.

They're compiled in zones for your added convenience and each item has its own easy-to-follow map reference.

All of Ireland is covered in a series of four ordnance survey maps to which this map belongs. The scale is 1 : 250,000, which is 4 centimetres to every 10 kilometres or about 1 inch to every 4 miles.

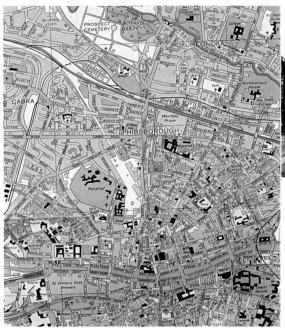

The steady growth in traffic and transport costs in towns and cities makes route-planning and identification of specific facilities such as car parks of prime importance to the commercial, business and casual traveller alike. The Ordnance Survey street maps, complete with indexes to street names and places of general interest, are designed to meet the needs of today's traveller.

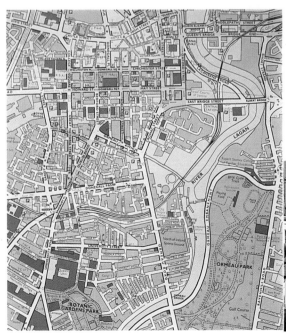

In the 1980s increasing interest in making the best use of leisure time and the consequent broadening of recreational interests led to the conception of a series of Outdoor Pursuits maps. These were designed in consultation with local Councils and various bodies with sporting or allied interests in specific locations. The resultant maps are therefore very much a reflection of the views and interests of the map user for whom they are intended.

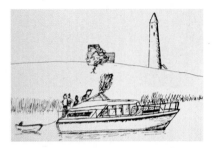

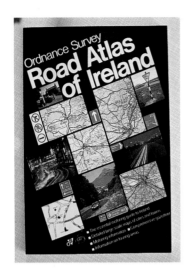

Co-operation between the two
Ordnance Surveys and other
bodies has resulted in the
publication of a number of joint-
venture products. Illustrated are
two Atlases and a Guide.

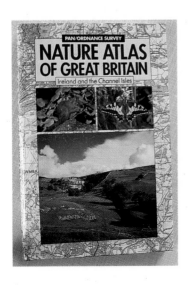

FROM PAPER TO MAGNETIC TAPE

Computer Aided Mapping System

Although computers and automatic draughting techniques were in use elsewhere in map production since the early 1970s it was not until some years later that the Ordnance Surveys in Ireland decided to introduce a computer aided mapping system. Having assessed both raster and vector formats, a system was installed in 1978 which had the ability to store a fully structured vector database. This capability has the flexibility to provide for both customers' and Ordnance Surveys' future requirements.

The growth of Information Technology led to the initiation in 1981 of a plan to convert OSNI mapping into digital form and to create a fully structured topographical database which would be the foundation for a Northern Ireland Geographic Information System (NIGIS). By May 1983 a Feasibility Study had been completed resulting in a recommendation that data conversion should proceed with a target date for completion of the mid-1990s.

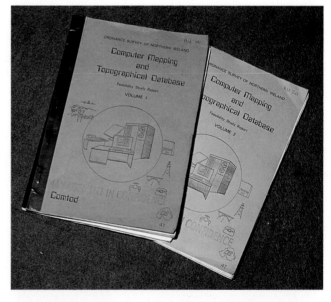

A Liaison Committee of representatives of various user groups was formed right at the beginning to ensure that all could work towards the common goal of a single integrated system of benefit to Northern Ireland as a whole. Included in the project are various departments of the government service as well as the major public utilities.

*OSNI Training in
Norway*

With acceptance of the digital mapping recommendations, training of staff in the
specialist skills to operate and maintain the selected system commenced. These were the
personnel who would carry out the acceptance tests in the systems installed, train other
staff and be responsible for future development work.

*OSI staff involved
in early development*

In Northern Ireland the decision to take the digital route dictated that a building suitable to house the new facilities should be found. Initially alterations to the existing headquarters building were considered but OS were operating from two separate locations in Belfast at this time and the most viable option was deemed to be the centralisation of all Belfast-based activities in one building. The result was a move in 1985 to Colby House at Stranmillis in Belfast.

At this time of revolution in map-making procedures it was perhaps more appropriate than ever that the new building should be named in honour of the first Director of Ordnance Survey in Ireland. However forward-looking the OS may be, there is never any hesitation in acknowledging the debt owed to its founding fathers.

In Dublin the computer system was installed in the old print building. It has now outgrown this building, and is connected to the other areas via an optic fibre network.

Computer Building, Ordnance Survey, Dublin

90

The Central Processing Unit (CPU) - The Heart of the System

The first essential in the creation of the digital database is the conversion to digital form of the existing archive of large-scale mapping information to fully structured digital form and the maintenance of the currency of that information.

Two methods are employed in the capture of the information - semi-automatic and manual. The data collected includes not only the geometry and text, etc., that make up the existing map archive, but also a wealth of other information. For example, a line on the map may be coded as side of road, footpath, hedge, administrative boundary, etc., because it represents each and every one of these features. The result of such coding is that a specific category of map detail can be extracted separately from the other information, and the user who wants only roads, or administrative boundaries, can view that detail without the distraction of any other type of feature. Associated textual information is also linked to an increasing number of features and provides additional data such as the full postal address of particular properties, type and density of vegetation, and date of survey.

The Cartographer working from the current map accurately converts the geometry, text and symbols to digital data. Using a high precision computer-linked digitizing tablet and cursor the co-ordinate value and feature code are recorded for each topographic detail point.

Manual Data Capture

A scanner reads the image through a sensor that travels over the surface of the map, and automatically converts the map detail into raster digital data. This is a very cost-effective means of data capture and is becoming increasingly sophisticated.

The raster data is converted to vector form and the cartographer then adds feature codes to the geometry and includes all text and symbols.

More automated methods now accommodate the addition of intelligence to the topographic data by the use of pattern, text and symbol recognition techniques, reducing the amount of manual intervention and cost of data capture.

Automatic Scanning

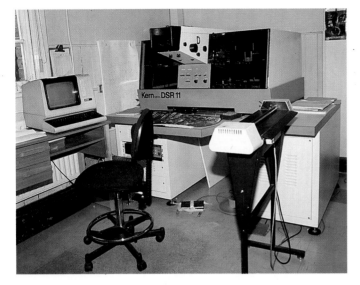

High precision analytical photogrammetric instruments are used to digitize map detail from aerial photography. Data captured in this manner contains three-dimensional co-ordinates in digital form which are stored on file. They are then plotted to produce master survey documents on which the field surveyors make additions or deletions as a result of detail being obscured or missing from the photography. These additions and deletions can be integrated by editing the data file captured by photogrammetry, thus maintaining the accuracy of the original plot.

*Digital Data Capture from
  Aerial Photography*

The developments in field surveying instrumentation have led to the use of Data Loggers for field digital data acquisition and this can be integrated with information already held in the database.

Data Logger

On completion of the digital conversion of map data the information may be viewed on a VDU or output via one of the plotting devices. The information is fully structured and can be plotted to customer requirements for content and scale.

The flatbed plotter uses pen, scribing tool or photohead attachments depending on the plotting medium used.

Flatbed Plotter

The electrostatic colour plotter plots standard and customised maps from the database on film or paper.

Electrostatic Plotter

Proof Plotter

The use of paper proof copies in the quality assurance process helps maintain the high standard and integrity of data which both digital and non-digital map customers traditionally expect from Ordnance Survey.

Ordnance Survey Belfast is the Remote Sensing Processing Centre for Northern Ireland. This enables study of the earth's resources from data obtained by aircraft and satellites. information on subjects as diverse as agriculture, oceanography, hydrology, the weather, and for planning can be readily gleaned from remotely-sensed imagery.

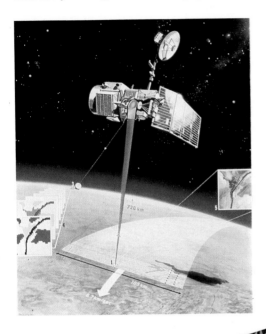

Interest in remote sensing will undoubtedly continue to grow. There is already widespread use of imagery from established satellites for a range of environmental applications. Satellite technology becomes increasingly sophisticated with one of the latest, the European Space Agency ESR1, using advanced microwave techniques to collect a range of global measurements and images.

By the turn of the century billions of bytes of data will be beaming down from even more sophisticated satellites - an exciting prospect for scientific, environmental and survey interests.

The digital large-scale products of both organisations are fully edge-matched to achieve ultimately a database of seamless survey information. They are then stored in a database management system with, in the case of OSNI, associated textual information (eg, full postal addresses of properties) attached. Most importantly, database currency is maintained. This is carried out as ground change occurs through the established range of survey revision systems. Future revision of the OS Dublin database will be from aerial photography using superimposition techniques.

Checking coding and edge matching using Mapman

Analytical stereoplotter with superimposition

CUSTOMER SERVICES

There are map shops at Dublin and Belfast headquarters where technical advice is also available.

Map Shop - Belfast

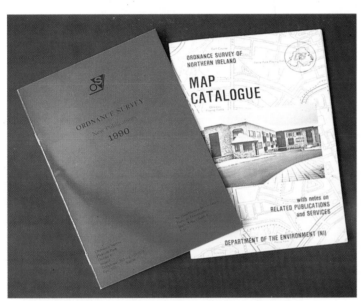

Both organisations have modern, well equipped reprographic facilities to service in-house needs and supply special services to customers' specifications.

Map Shop - Dublin

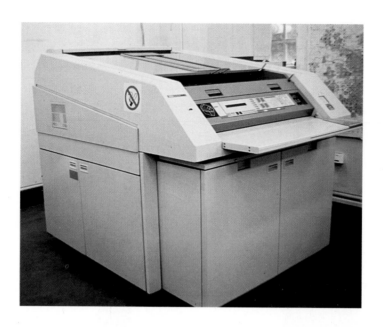

Plain Paper Printer

Ordnance Survey holds approximately 40,000 large scale maps covering Ireland. In the past, storage of huge map stocks consumed valuable resources. Today, at both headquarters, sophisticated plain paper copiers provide a print-on-demand service from 'master' maps. This ensures continuity of supply whilst avoiding the problem of stock control.

This cost-effective system which can provide accurate reproductions and enlargements, gives a choice of scale not previously available.

Traditional skills and modern equipment are used to produce a range of mounted and laminated map products.

Dry Mounting Press

98

Four Colour Printing Press

The printing division of Ordnance Survey Dublin has been systematically re-equipped with new machinery since 1988. A large format four-colour printing press was installed in early 1988. This has since been complemented with a large format folding machine in the print finishing area. OS Dublin now prints a large range of map products for itself and other customers.

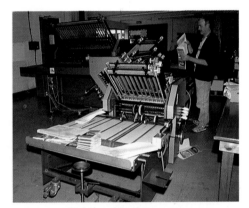

Folding Machine

Some Products Printed in Dublin

The introduction of major computerized systems by both Ordnance Surveys has opened up a whole new challenging and exciting era of customer service with virtually unlimited potential. This revolution puts both organisations at the forefront of the development and exploitation of Geographic Information System (GIS) technology. OS Dublin plan to create two mapping databases, one containing large-scales information to suit the GIS requirements of local authorities and major utilities, and the second a medium/small-scales database to support the needs of GIS for resource management and tourism. In preparation for the widespread use of digital map data OSI are represented on the Department of Energy Committee dealing with GIS requirements for the utilities and municipalities. OSNI are meeting major customer needs through NIGIS - The Northern Ireland Geographic Information System. This is a highly innovative, countrywide project involving a developing computer-based network of databases, with appropriate communication links, through which the spatially referenced data holdings of all the main government and public utility partners can be linked using the common geographic location provided by the OSNI topographic database.

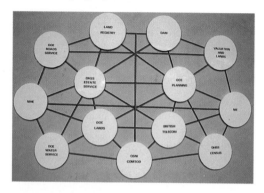

NIGIS
Network

All information, whether it relates to, for example, a water pipe, a house or an employment statistic, has one thing in common - location. This location can be referenced by a common system of geographical co-ordinates. The OSNI database contains not only geographical co-ordinates but also associated textual information including the full postal addresses of property elements, and this enhancement of locational data provides a key component in NIGIS.

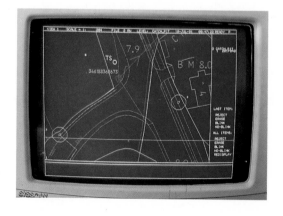

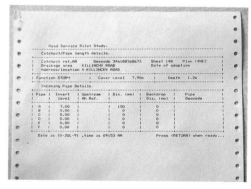

Screen display of plant and associated records

Given the correct data held and maintained in an appropriate form, GIS applications are constrained only by the imagination. In a typical underground plant maintenance situation a NIGIS utility partner could display topographic data on screen and by accessing, for example, the databases of the organisations responsible for water and electricity, combine this information for interrogation and if necessary, produce a working plan for use on site. Improved efficiency of access to relevant data will enable greatly enhanced co-ordination among the parties involved thus minimizing duplication of effort on-site and the risk of unnecessary and expensive damage to existing services.

Typical NIGIS application

Another typical GIS application allows the Planning Service to display topographic information covering a planning application, link the textual details of this to the site under review, and interrogate NIGIS for details of ownership, adjoining properties, site services, etc. The result is more enlightened planning decisions based on full access to all pertinent facts.

PLANNING APPLICATIONS

APPLICATION NO : X/89/0600 APPLICATION TYPE : O DATE VALID : 12-Aug-1989	ADDRESS : HOUSE NO. STREET BALLYDRAIN RD CITY COMBER POSTCODE BT235SR
GEOCODE :346640368315	OS_SHEET : 148155NW3

PROPOSAL :SITE FOR ICE-CREAM MANUFACTURING UNIT

PROPOSED USE :I
NAT OF DEVEL :B

CONDITIONS :CONTRARY TO THE DEPARTMENTS POLICY REGARDING GREEN BELTS

DECISION : RF
DATE: 6-Dec-1989

APPEAL DECISION	APPEAL DATE OF DECISION	APPEAL DATE

Any GIS database must be both accurate and current. In the case of Northern Ireland each NIGIS partner is responsible for the capturing and updating of its own information and making it available to others over the network. Duplication is avoided and the originator controls the data content.

Full co-operation among users is essential to any GIS application, regardless of size. OS Dublin ensure this through their involvement on the Department of Energy Committee, while in Northern Ireland, Liaison Committees, under the chairmanship of OSNI, meet regularly to guide NIGIS development. These Committees have been further supplemented by the creation of a NIGIS Unit at OSNI to act as focal point for future development and support of NIGIS partners.

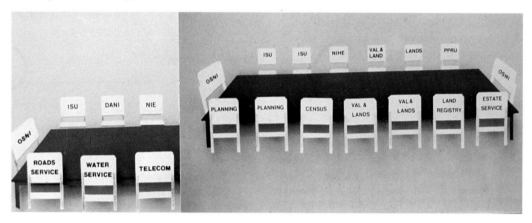

NIGIS Liaison Committees

In Northern Ireland an on-going series of user pilot projects, led and hosted by OSNI, is establishing the potential and these projects are leading to initial introduction of GIS technology within the user organisations concerned. Once proven, systems will be extended to cover all of Northern Ireland.

Pilot Project

Both Ordnance Surveys are in no doubt that GIS is one of the management tools of the future and are determined to ensure that the geographic foundation, so essential to successful exploitation of the technology for the benefit of all in Ireland, North and South, is not found wanting.

So this is the Ordnance Survey in Ireland today. There is much to celebrate in the development of map-making over 200 years. This review has recorded some of the high-lights and some of the heartaches; some of the turning-points and some of the routine. Although the techniques have changed almost beyond belief and certainly beyond recognition, the aim has remained constant - the provision of a service, a total quality service, to the community at large. It is a story not just of technological improvement, but also of the unstinting efforts of those involved in the survey and mapping of Ireland in establishing and maintaining standards that are second to none.

SUGGESTED FURTHER READING

Title	Author	Publisher	Year of Publication
The Early Years of the Ordnance Survey	C Close	The Institution of Royal Engineers	1926
History in the Ordnance Map	J H Andrews	Ordnance Survey of Ireland	1974
A Paper Landscape	J H Andrews	Oxford University Press	1975
A History of the Ordnance Survey	W A Seymour	Wm Dawson & Sons Ltd	1980
Plantation Acres	J H Andrews	Ulster Historical Foundation	1985